Wallace & Gromit's
Christmas Crackers

W0007881

B🌲XTREE

WALLACE & GROMIT'S USELESS XMAS TRIVIA FACT:
The cracker originated in 1840 when Tom Smith discovered that people
in London liked receiving gifts of sweets wrapped up in a twist of paper

First published 2002 by Boxtree
an imprint of Pan Macmillan Ltd
Pan Macmillan, 20 New Wharf Road, London N1 9RR
Basingstoke and Oxford
Associated companies throughout the world
www.panmacmillan.com

ISBN 0 7522 1511 6

Produced under license by Aardman Animations
© and ™ Aardman/Wallace and Gromit Ltd 2002

Text © Macmillan Publishers Ltd 2002

1 3 5 7 9 8 6 4 2

A CIP catalogue record for this book is available from
the British Library.

Design by Dan Newman, Perfect Bound
Text by Natalie Jerome & Dawn Burnett

Printed by Proost, Belgium

Welcome to Wallace and Gromit's countdown to Xmas!

The date
25th December

The place
62 West Wallaby Street

The Event
CHRISTMAS DAY!

1 December

Gromit realises that there are only 24 shopping days til Xmas.

Letter to Santa:
My Christmas present list

Cornflake bowl
(no cracks)

dog brush (new)

Knit One, Purl One
(Penguin 1996)

2 DECEMBER

Check what others are going to buy for Xmas. Gromit remembers last year when someone stole his idea.

Wallace's Xmas present list:-
Brown wool trousers (new pair)
green jumper (spare)
Wing Nuts - A History
(Macmillan 1991)

3 DECEMBER

Book tickets for the Xmas pantomime. Gromit has always fancied himself as Dick Whittington.

4 DECEMBER

Christmas is a time
for forgiveness
and goodwill
to all men.

5 DECEMBER

Make sure you beat the Xmas rush to the shops. Wallace finds his scooter 'just the ticket' for avoiding traffic!

6 DECEMBER

If you're still not sure what your loved ones want for Xmas, stick to something safe.

Cheese, for instance.

7&8 DECEMBER

Watch your drink during the Xmas festivities. Wallace cunningly disguises his festive tipple in a teacup.

9 DECEMBER

Avoid stressful situations at Xmas - arguments are all too common during the festive season.

Stocking fillers (for Wendolene)

Mini bottle of sherry, manicure set, gloves, satsuma

10 DECEMBER

Gromit quickly discovers that Christmas can bring out the competitive spirit in many people.

Stocking fillers (for Wallace)

Nuts, satsuma, cheese (all varieties), mini bottle of port, socks

11 DECEMBER

Practice your dance moves in time for the Xmas party. Gromit is a demon at the Macarena.

12 DECEMBER

Start cooking in preparation for the big day. Ensure you make some extra food in case of unexpected guests.

13 DECEMBER

Wallace begins to panic as he realises his game of hide-and-seek with Gromit has got out of hand.

FESTIVE CHEESE ON TOAST

- Slice or crumble lots of cheese (preferably Wensleydale) onto wholemeal bread, top with cranberry sauce (instead of Branston pickle).
- Place under a hot grill until brown and bubbling.

14&15 DECEMBER

Give yourself plenty of time
to get ready for your
Xmas party.

Wallace discovers to his
horror that his hairdresser is
booked up until New Year.

16 December

Spread a little Christmas cheer by singing carols to the neighbours.

Mulled Wine (Wallace's fave Xmas tipple)

- Red wine (a nice claret will do)
- Fruit
- Cloves
- Cinnamon

Mix and warm in a saucepan without boiling.
(Guaranteed to keep you warm on those cold winter nights).

17 DECEMBER

Some people might not take your efforts at carol singing as seriously as you might have hoped.

18 DECEMBER

Gromit likes to keep things simple as he prepares to switch on the Xmas tree lights.

WALLACE & GROMIT'S USELESS XMAS TRIVIA FACT:
The Xmas Tree as we now know it, was introduced by German reformer Martin Luther. Xmas tree lights are meant to mimic stars shining through fir trees.

19 DECEMBER

Remember not to get too carried away with your decorations – your lights could end up resembling Oxford Street.

20 DECEMBER

Gromit
62 WEST WALLABY ST
WIGAN
LANCS D83 BB6

It's the last day for posting
Xmas cards. If you have as
many friends as Wallace
and Gromit, it pays to
be organised.

WALLACE & GROMIT'S USELESS XMAS TRIVIA FACT:
The earliest printed Xmas card was made in 1843 by Sir Henry Cole.
Sir Henry decided to have a card printed that he could send to
relatives and friends.

21&22 DECEMBER

Remember the festive season does strange things to people and some might get a little frisky...

WALLACE & GROMIT'S USELESS XMAS TRIVIA FACT:
Traditionally if a man and a woman kiss under the mistletoe they are blessed with good luck. Kissing under the mistletoe has come from a custom that was once found only in England.

23 DECEMBER

Activities during the festive
season are essential –
otherwise boredom can
easily set in.

STIRRING THE XMAS PUD

Gromit's favourite Xmas tradition. If he gets his wish, he might find
that Wallace has 'lost' his tape of 'You've Lost That Loving Feeling'
that he always plays at this time of year.

24 DECEMBER

Try not to frighten the neighbours when you deliver presents in your Santa Claus outfit.

WALLACE & GROMIT'S USELESS XMAS TRIVIA FACT:
The story of Father Christmas or Santa Claus has ancient European roots. St. Nicholas was the inspiration for the modern Santa Claus, but St Nicholas was himself derived from pagan gift givers.

25 DECEMBER

This was not what Wallace had in mind when he said he wanted a big juicy bird!

WALLACE & GROMIT'S USELESS XMAS TRIVIA FACT:
Before turkey took over in the 1600s, popular Xmas delicacies were goose and cockerel and in the houses of the rich, peacock and swan.

26 DECEMBER

**Gromit has over-indulged
on the brussel sprouts again.
Remember excessive
wind could get
you in the
dog house!**